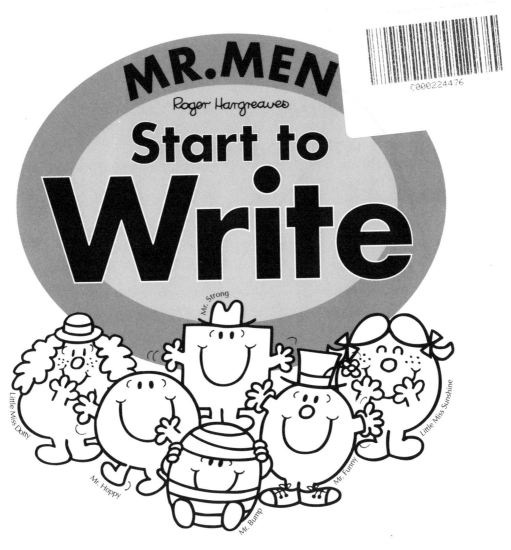

MR.MEN
Roger Hargreaves

Start to
Write

Illustrated by Adam Hargreaves

Exercises devised by John Malam

Educational consultant: Betty Root

Betty Root has a lifetime of experience in education, as a teacher, lecturer and consultant. She has written, or acted as advisor on, numerous books for primary and pre-school children.

MR.MEN   LITTLE MISS

MR. MEN and LITTLE MISS™ © THOIP (a Chorion Company)

www.ilovemrmen.co.uk

Mr. Men and Little Miss™ Text and illustrations © 2011 THOIP (a Chorion company).
Original creation by Roger Hargreaves
Illustrated by Adam Hargreaves
Printed and published under licence from Price Stern Sloan Inc., Los Angeles.

First published in Great Britain in 2004
This edition published in 2011 by Dean, an imprint of Egmont UK Limited
239 Kensington High Street, London W8 6SA

ISBN 978 0 6035 6265 5
7 9 10 8
Printed in Italy

This is Mr Strong.
He is learning to write.
Follow the lines with your pencil.
Start at the arrows.

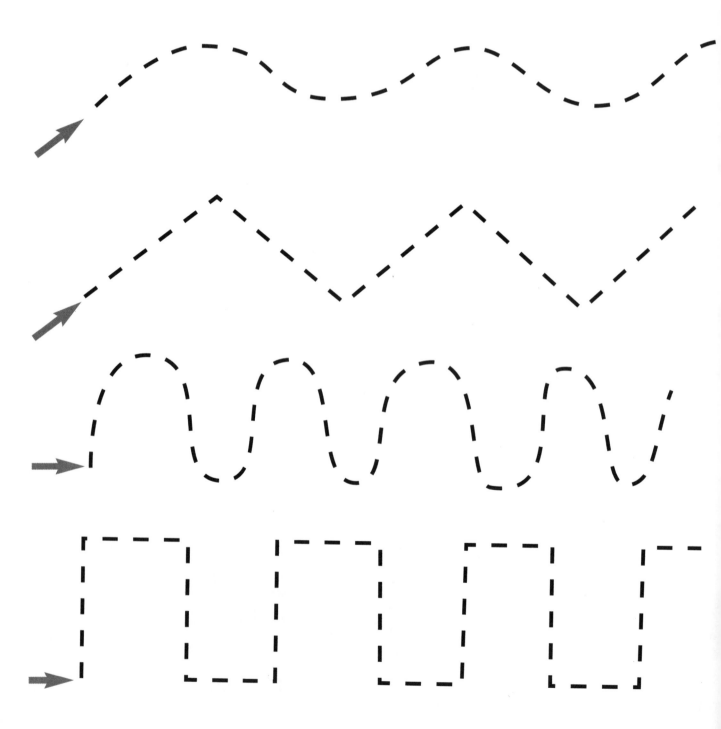

Draw a line to show Mr Strong
the way to his house.
Try not to cross the lines.

This is Little Miss Neat.
She does everything as neatly
as she can.
Finish drawing her brushes.
Be as neat as you can.
Start at the arrows.

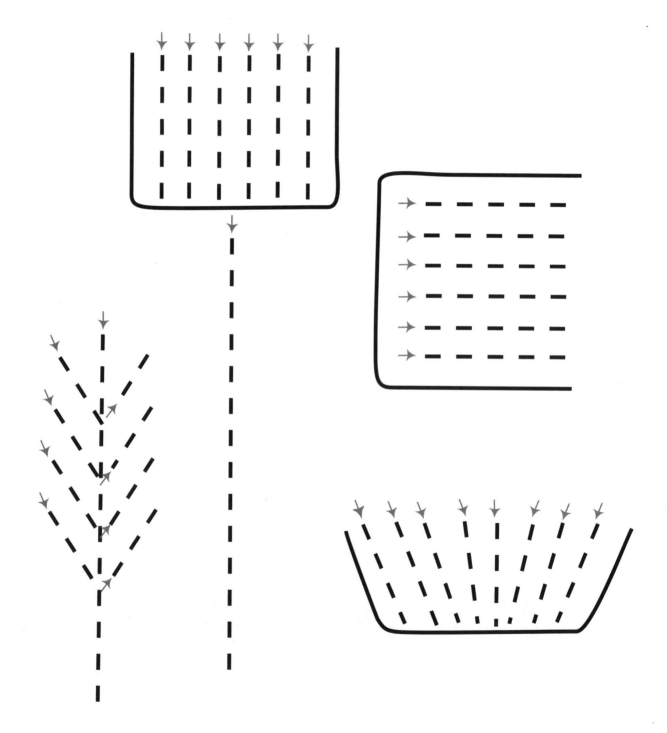

Little Miss Neat is cleaning her bath.
She's making lots of bubbles.
Draw the bubbles.
Start at the arrows.

This is Little Miss Brainy.
She is very good at making patterns.
Are you?
Draw between the lines.

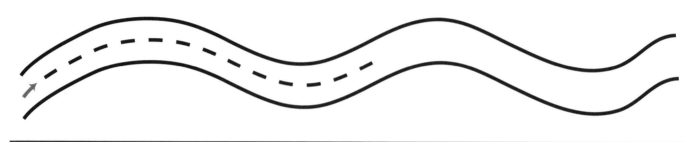

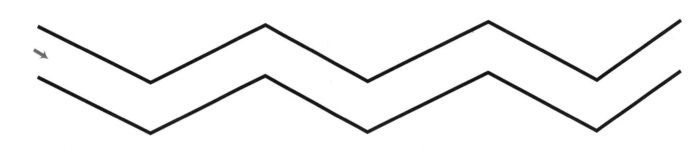

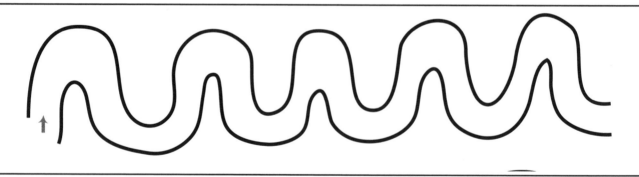

Little Miss Brainy knows the colours of the rainbow.
Help her to draw the rainbow.
Start at the arrows. Then colour it in.

red

orange

yellow

green

blue

indigo

violet

Little Miss Shy and Little Miss Sunshine are having a ride in a hot air balloon. Finish the picture.

Little Miss Shy can write lots
of letters.
You can write them too.
Start at the arrows.

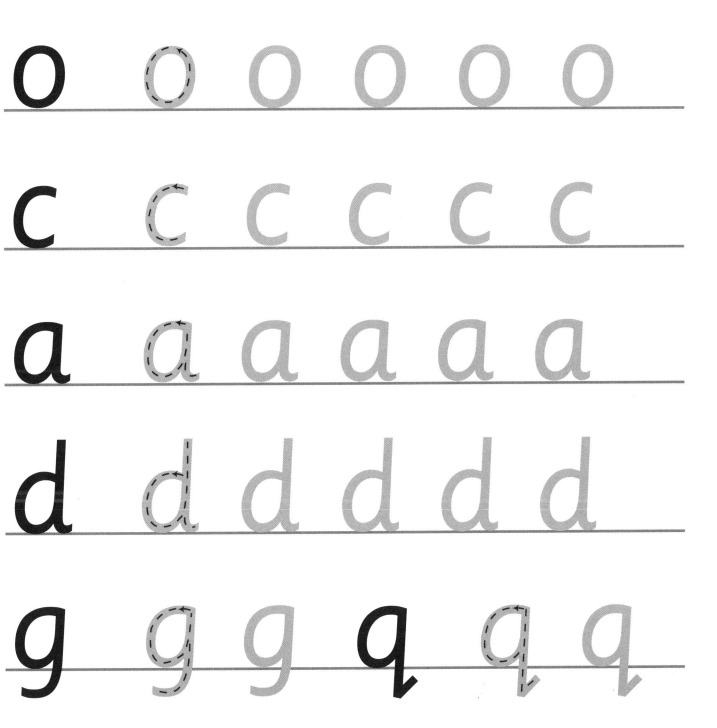

o o o o o o o

c c c c c c c

a a a a a a a

d d d d d d d

g g g g q q q

This is Mr Tall.
He is as tall as a house.
Draw the house.

Mr Tall can write all these letters.
You can write them too.
Start at the arrows.

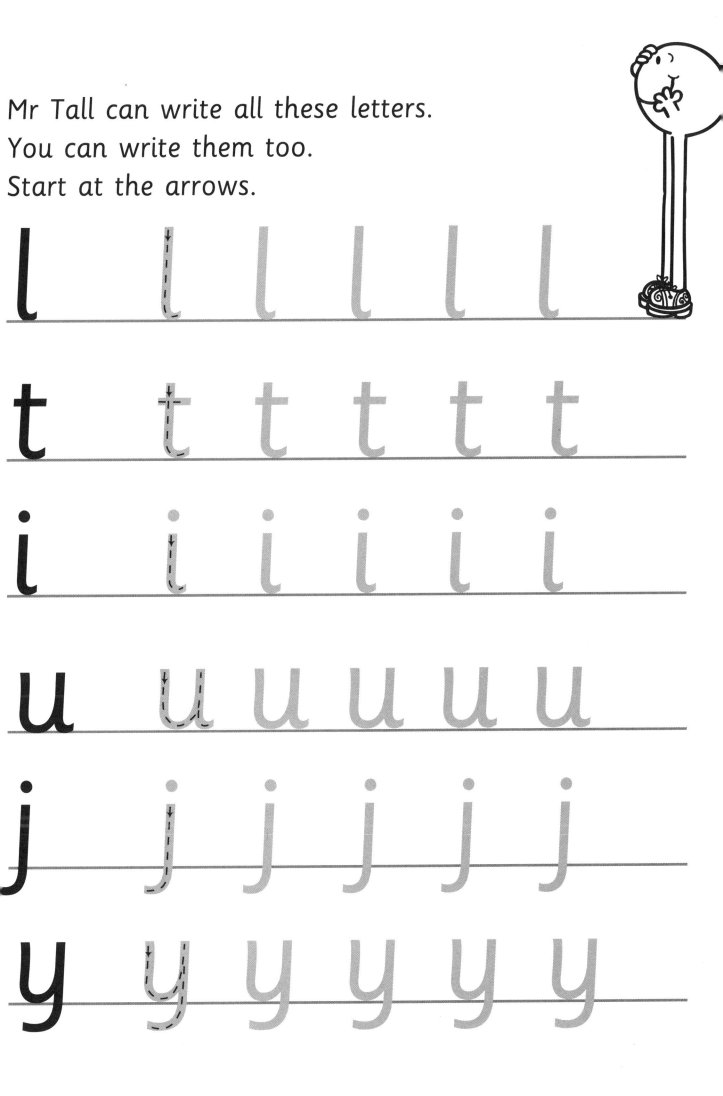

Little Miss Quick likes to ski.
Draw the patterns on these flags.
Start at the arrows.

Little Miss Quick likes to practise her letters.
Help her write these letters.
Start at the arrows.

V   V V V V V V

X   X X X X X X

W   W W W W W W

z   z z z z z z

k   k k k k k k

Mr Bounce and Little Miss Somersault are bouncing in space!
Follow their bounces with your pencil.

Now you can write the letters.

h h h h h h h

m m m m m m m

n n n n n n n

p p p p p p p

r r r r r r r

b b b b b b b

Here is Mr Funny in a sailing hat!
Follow the waves with your pencil.
Draw a pattern on the sails.

e e e e e e

Now write the letters and
finish the words.

f f f f f f f

s s s s s s

sea   sail   flag

This is Mr Small.
He can write all the letters.
You can write with him.
Start at the arrows.
Have fun looking for him in the pictures.

a a a a a a **apple**

b b b b b b **ball**

c c c c c c **cup**

d d d d d d **dog**

e e e e e e **egg**

f f f f f f   **fish**

g g g g g g   **gate**

h h h h h h   **hat**

i i i i i i   **igloo**

j j j j j j   **jelly**

k k k k k k   **key**

l l l l l l   **lion**

m m m m m m   mouse

n n n n n n   nest

o o o o o o   octopu

p p p p p p   pear

q q q q q q   queen

r r r r r r   rabbit

s s s s s s   sun

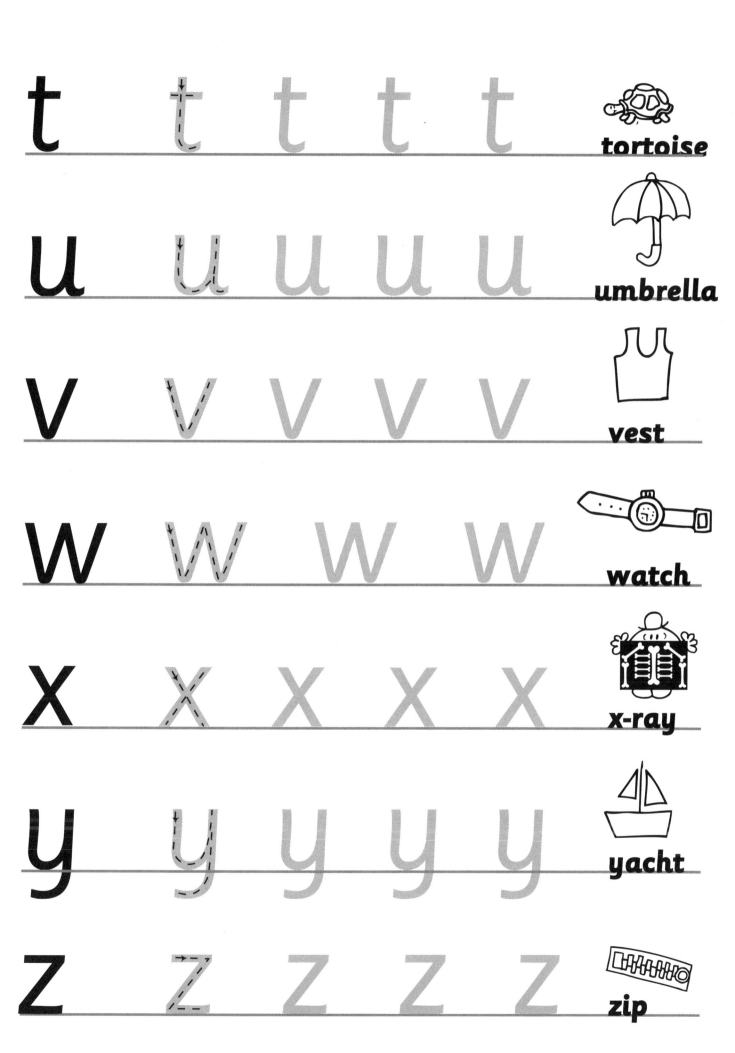

t t t t t **tortoise**

u u u u u **umbrella**

v v v v v **vest**

w w w w w **watch**

x x x x x **x-ray**

y y y y y **yacht**

z z z z z **zip**

This is Mr Clever.
Here are some of his favourite words.
Copy the words.

hat

clock

- - - - -

- - - - - -

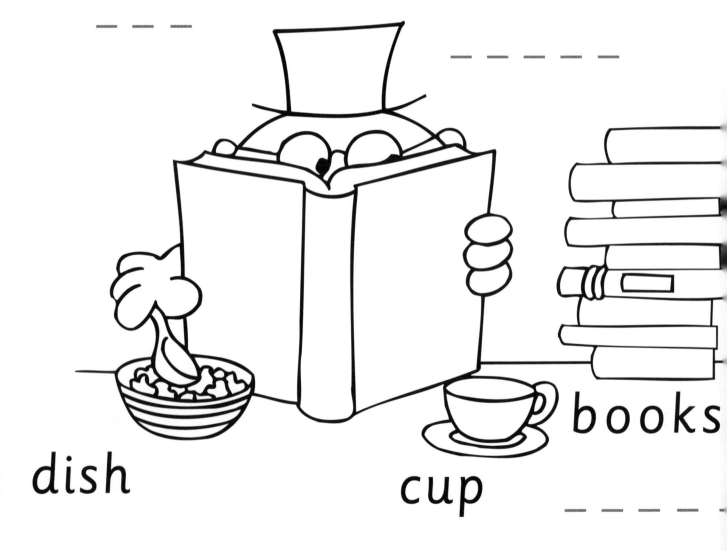

dish

cup

books

- - - -

- - - -

Mr Clever's
Writing Award

Presented to:

....

....

(write your name here)

for finishing this book.

signed.....................(parent/guardian)

Notes to parents

Get a good start with the Mr Men.

This book is part of a series designed to prepare children for starting school. The following skills are covered in this book:

- pencil control using patterns in readiness for writing letters;

- recognising the shapes of the lower-case (small) letters of the alphabet;

- an understanding of the directions (start and finish points) used to write the letters;

- practice at writing letters.

The aim is to build confidence and make learning as much fun as possible. By working on these activities with your child you can offer help and encouragement, and share the fun. Here are a few simple ways that you can help your child to learn.

- Start at the beginning of the book and work through each page. The activities get gradually more difficult, building on what your child has learnt.

- Short sessions are more likely to hold your child's interest, so do not try to do too much in one go. You might start with just one activity. Stop if your child is losing concentration or an activity seems too difficult; you can always come back to it later.

- Be sure to reward your child's efforts. If your child feels successful, he/she will be keen to learn next time.

- Discuss each activity with your child to make certain that it is understood before any writing takes place. Asking questions and puzzling out the activities together is an important part of the learning process.